Key Stage 1

English Practice Papers

Carol Matchett

Write your name in the box before you start the practice papers.

Name

After you have finished each test and had it marked, your marks should go in these boxes.

Reading Paper 1	
Reading Paper 2	
Total	

Grammar, Punctuation and Spelling Paper 1	
Grammar, Punctuation and Spelling Paper 2	
Total	

Schofield&Sims

Contents

Note for adults helping with Grammar, Punctuation and Spelling

The script for Grammar, Punctuation and Spelling Paper 1 should be removed from the book before the child starts the test.

General instructions

This book contains the following four practice papers.

- Reading Paper 1 (30 minutes)
- Reading Paper 2 (40 minutes)
- Grammar, Punctuation and Spelling Paper 1: spelling (15 minutes)
- Grammar, Punctuation and Spelling Paper 2: questions (20 minutes)

It is best to do the papers in the order they appear in the book, but don't do all the tests at the same time. Have a break between tests.

Before you start a test

When you are ready to do one of the practice papers, find a quiet place where you can concentrate.

Make sure you have enough time to complete the practice paper before you start it. The Key Stage 1 tests are not strictly timed but once started it is best to complete a paper without stopping.

Ask an adult to read through the instructions page for the test you are about to do. Listen carefully and make sure you understand what to do. Ask questions if you are not sure.

When you are ready to begin, turn to the first page of the practice paper.

During the test

Work through the test on your own.

The questions in Grammar, Punctuation and Spelling Paper 1 will be read out loud by the adult who is helping you.

Work through all the questions. Read the questions carefully and try your best to answer them all. Think carefully. If you can't answer a question, move to the next one – you can come back to it later. Check your answers so you don't make careless mistakes.

Stop at the end of the test. This is clearly marked 'End of test'.

Don't look at the answers before or during the test.

After the test

Ask an adult to mark your practice paper using the answers and mark scheme on pages 39–50. They should then write your total mark in the boxes on pages 3 and 51.

Look at any questions you couldn't do or answered incorrectly. These are topics you need to revise. The Schofield & Sims **Key Stage 1 English Revision Guide** will help you with this.

Instructions for the Reading test

The Key Stage 1 English Reading test is split into two papers.

Reading Paper 1 has the text and the questions on the same page (pages 9–21).

Reading Paper 2 has a separate Reading Booklet (a pull-out section in the centre of this book) and question paper (pages 22–26).

Instructions for Reading Paper 1

In Reading Paper 1, you will find a story and some information to read. The text to read is at the top of each page and there are some questions for you to answer below it.

This test will take about 30 minutes but it is not a timed test.

What to do

At the start of the test you will find a list of 'Useful words' and a 'Practice page' with some practice questions. There is another list of useful words and a further practice page on pages 17–18. Ask an adult to help you with these practice pages. The adult can read the words and text to you on these pages and help you answer the questions. Listen carefully as this will help you to read and understand some important words.

The practice questions show you the sorts of questions you will answer in the test. For most questions, you write your answer on a line or choose the right answer and put a tick in the box next to it.

You will find some different types of question to answer, such as putting numbers in boxes to order events or drawing lines to match answers.

Once you have gone through the first practice page (page 9) you are ready to begin the test. Continue reading the text and answering the questions on pages 10–16 on your own. Remember to think carefully about the answers you write and which boxes you tick.

When you get to the second practice page, on page 18, you can ask an adult to help you read it. Then continue reading the text and answering the questions on pages 19–21 on your own.

Stop at the end of page 21. The end of the test is clearly marked.

Note for adults helping with Reading Paper 1

You should read the lists of 'Useful words' to the child and discuss the meaning of these words.

You should also read the text on the two practice pages and help the child to answer the practice questions on these pages. You should **not** help with reading anything else on the practice papers.

Instructions for Reading Paper 2

For Reading Paper 2, you will need the separate Reading Booklet, which is a pull-out section in the centre of this book. Before you begin the test, ask an adult to pull this booklet out from the centre of the book.

The questions to go with the Reading Booklet are in Practice Paper 2, which starts on page 22. This is where you write your answers.

The test should take you about 40 minutes but it is not a timed test.

What to do

In the Reading Booklet, you will find there are three pieces of text. In the practice paper, there are questions to answer about each piece of text. Work your way through the test by reading each piece of text and then answering the questions about it.

The practice paper clearly tells you which questions are about which piece of text. For example: 'Questions 1–4 are about **On the bridge** (Reading Booklet page 2)'.

Each question also tells you the page in the Reading Booklet where the answer can be found. Look out for this information at the end of each question.

As in Paper 1, for most questions, you write the answer on a line or choose the right answer and put a tick in a box next to it. Again you will find some different types of question to answer, such as:

- putting ticks in a table to show if a statement is true or false
- drawing lines to match answers
- filling in information in a table.

Try to answer all of the questions. If you can't answer a question, move to the next one and come back to that one later.

Stop at the end of the test on page 26. The end of the test is clearly marked.

There are no practice pages in Reading Paper 2 so make sure you understand what you have to do before you begin.

Note for adults helping with Reading Paper 2

There are no lists of useful words, practice pages or practice questions with Reading Paper 2.

You can explain that the question types will be the same as those already seen in Reading Paper 1. Do **not** help with reading any part of the Reading Booklet or the questions about it.

DO NOT TURN OVER THIS PAGE UNTIL YOU ARE READY TO START READING PAPER 1

Reading Paper 1

Useful words

jackal

dye

washerman

Practice page 1

The Blue Jackal

A story from India

Once, a jackal went looking for food. He could not find anything to eat in the forest, so he went into the nearby village. It was midnight and everyone was asleep.

Practice questions

a Why did the jackal go into the village?

Tick **one**.

He was tired. ☐

He was lost. ☐

He was looking for food. ☐

It was late. ☐

b What time of day was it?

....

please turn over

Reading Paper 1 *continued*

The jackal saw the open window in the washerman's house. He peeped inside and saw lots of pots. 'There must be something to eat in those,' he said to himself.

He jumped down into the house, but…

Splash!

He landed in a tub full of blue dye left beneath the window.

He climbed out, but his fur was now bright blue! He tried to lick himself clean but the blue dye would not come off.

---

1 What did the jackal think was in the pots he saw?

....

2 Where was the tub of blue dye?

Tick **two**.

outside the washerman's house	☐
inside the washerman's house	☐
by the door	☐
under the window	☐
on the fire	☐

Slowly, the jackal made his way back to the forest. 'I do not look like a jackal now,' he sighed. 'Everyone will laugh at me.'

But all the other animals were amazed when they saw the blue jackal.

'What is this animal?' they asked.

'It must be some strange new beast,' they said.

And they all ran away in terror.

---

3 How do you know the jackal was upset about his blue fur?

....

4 Find and copy the word that tells you the other animals were frightened by the blue jackal.

....

pages 10–11 total

please turn over

When the jackal saw all the animals running away, he had an idea.

He called back all the frightened animals and said, 'Oh beasts of the forest, blue is the colour of kings. From today, I am your king.'

All the animals bowed down. 'You are our king!' they said.

'What a grand colour I am,' smiled the blue jackal.

---

5 How did the jackal feel when he saw the other animals running away?

Tick **one**.

sad ☐

upset ☐

pleased ☐

angry ☐

6 What did the animals do after the blue jackal spoke to them?

....

7 Why did the jackal say 'What a grand colour I am'?

....

....

The jackal made all the animals serve him.

The lions and tigers hunted for his food. The elephants fetched his water. The mice found soft grass for him to sleep on. The birds sang for him. The monkeys fanned him with leaves.

The jackal just sat on his forest throne.

8 The jackal made all the animals serve him. Draw lines to match the animals to how they served him.

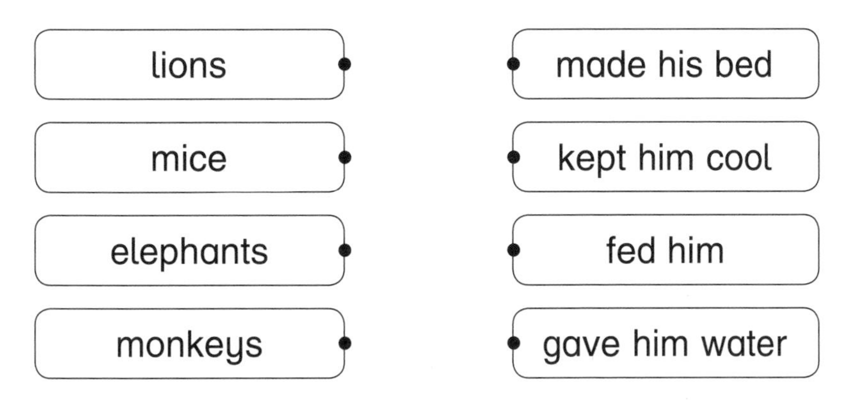

pages 12–13 total

please turn over

But the blue jackal would not go near the other jackals. He wanted nothing to do with them. He feared they knew his secret.

One day, he heard the other jackals talking. 'He may be blue, but he is still only a jackal like us,' they said. 'The other animals spoil him.'

At once, the blue jackal told the tigers to chase the other jackals out of the forest.

---

9 Why was the blue jackal worried about the other jackals?

....

10 What did the other jackals say about the blue jackal?

Tick **one**.

He was treated too well.	☐
He was treated badly.	☐
He was a special jackal.	☐
He was a good friend.	☐

Many moons later, the jackals were sitting on a faraway hillside howling at the stars.

In the forest, the blue jackal heard them howling. Without thinking, he sat up and began to howl back just like any other jackal.

When the other animals heard that howl, they knew at once he was just a plain old jackal.

'This jackal has fooled us,' the lion said. 'He must be punished.'

They chased the blue jackal away and he was never seen in the forest again.

---

11 *...they knew at once he was just a plain old jackal.*
What does the word 'plain' mean in this sentence?

Tick **one**.

not pretty	☐	not clever	☐
not blue	☐	not special	☐

12 The animals punished the jackal because...

	Tick **one**.
he was different to them.	☐
he was a bad king.	☐
he pretended to be something he was not.	☐
he was dyed blue.	☐

pages 14–15 total

please turn over

13 Number the sentences below from 1 to 4 to show the order they happen in the story.

The first one is done for you.

The jackal returned to the forest. ☐

The jackal's fur was dyed blue. 1

The jackal was tricked by the other jackals. ☐

The jackal tricked the other animals. ☐

page total

Useful words

Antarctic

emperor penguins

ocean

please turn over

Practice page 2

Penguins

Penguins are amazing birds. They live in the Antarctic in a land of snow and ice. They cannot fly, but they are superb swimmers.

Practice questions

c Where do penguins live?

....

d What do penguins do very well?

Tick **one**.

fly ☐

sing ☐

swim ☐

ski ☐

Reading Paper 1 *continued*

On land, penguins stand upright and waddle about. Some penguins find that the best way to travel across the snow is to slide on their fat bellies using their wings to push and steer.

---

14 How do some penguins use their wings to help them travel on land?

Tick **one**.

to help them fly	☐	to help them walk	☐
to help them swim	☐	to help them slide	☐

15 Give **two** parts of the body that help to keep the penguin warm.

1. ....

2. ....

page 19 total

please turn over

Penguins can dive deep down into the ocean. They catch all their food underwater and need to swim very fast. They use their wings as flippers to help them glide through the water. Their spiky tongues help grip the slippery fish.

---

16 Which word in the text describes what the penguin's tongue is like?

Tick **one**.

slippery ☐ grip ☐

spiky ☐ glide ☐

17 Why do penguins need to be good swimmers?

....

In spring, emperor penguins walk far across the snow and ice to lay their eggs. The mother penguin then waddles off to the sea to find food. The father stays and takes care of the egg. Emperor penguins do not build nests so for two months the father balances the egg on his feet, keeping it off the ice. He keeps the egg tucked under a cosy flap of skin.

---

18 Which of the following sentences is true?

Tick **one**.

- Emperor penguins build nests in spring. ☐
- Emperor penguins lay eggs in nests. ☐
- Emperor penguins lay eggs in spring. ☐
- The mother penguin takes care of the egg. ☐
- The father penguin goes to find food. ☐

19 Why must the penguin keep the egg off the ice?

....

20 Find and copy a word that tells you the egg is warm under the flap of skin.

....

pages 20–21 total

END OF TEST

Total score for Reading Paper 1
Write this score in the box on pages 3 and 51.

Reading Paper 2

Questions 1–4 are about the poem 'On the bridge' (Reading Booklet page 2)

1 Where is the bridge in the poem? (page 2)

Tick **one**.

over a pond ☐ over the sea ☐

over a river ☐ over a railway ☐

2 Write **three** creatures that the writer wishes to see. (page 2)

1. ....

2. ....

3. ....

3 *I want to see his great round eyes* (page 2)

What does the word 'great' mean in this line?

Tick **one**.

excellent ☐ many ☐

big ☐ important ☐

4 The poet thinks of **two** things she would like to do while standing on the bridge. Explain what these two ideas are. (page 2)

1. ....

....

2. ....

....

Questions 5–12 are about the story 'The Cloud-Eater' (Reading Booklet pages 3–5)

5 Why did the Cloud-Eater live at the top of a tall mountain? (page 3)

....

6 Find and copy **two** words that describe how dry the ground was. (page 3)

1. ....

2. ....

7 Why did the boy decide to try to kill the Cloud-Eater? (page 3)

....

8 Why was the boy's grandmother proud of him? (page 4)

....

9 How did the boy find his way easily up the mountain path? (page 4)

....

pages 22–23 total

please turn over

10 How did the boy know that the Cloud-Eater was dead? (page 5)

....

11 The feathers helped the boy to defeat the Cloud-Eater. Draw lines to match the feathers to the help they gave him. (pages 4–5)

the red feather	helped him get close to the Cloud-Eater
the blue feather	helped him find the gopher
the yellow feather	helped him fire the arrow
the black feather	helped him ask the way

12 Think about all you have read. (pages 3–5)

What do you think is likely to happen when the boy returns to the village? Give a reason.

I think ....

....

because ....

....

Questions 13–18 are about the article 'Tomatoes' (Reading Booklet pages 6–8)

(page 6)

13 Why did people in Britain not eat tomatoes at first?

....

(page 6)

14 Why are tomatoes sometimes grown in greenhouses?

....

(page 7)

15 Find and copy **three** ways to use tomatoes uncooked.

1. ....
2. ....
3. ....

(page 8)

16 The earliest ketchup was made from…

Tick **one**.

tomatoes. ☐

peaches. ☐

mushrooms. ☐

fish. ☐

pages 24–25 total

please turn over

17 How do you know that the food festival 'La Tomatina' is very popular? (page 8)

....

18 Put a tick in the box to show which sentences are true and which are false. (pages 7–8)

The information says that...	True	False
tomatoes are vegetables.		
tomatoes are the fruit of the tomato plant.		
the bright colours in tomatoes are good for you.		
today all tomatoes are red.		
tomato plants are not good to eat.		

END OF TEST

page total

Total score for Reading Paper 2
Write this score in the box on pages 3 and 51.

English
Reading Booklet
Key Stage 1 English Practice Papers

Contents

Schofield & Sims

On the bridge

If I could see a little fish –
That is what I just now wish;
I want to see his great round eyes
Always open in surprise.

I wish a water rat would glide
Slowly to the other side;
Or a dancing spider sit
On the yellow flags a bit.

I think I'll get some stones to throw,
And watch the pretty circles show.
Or shall we sail a flower-boat,
And watch it slowly – slowly float?

That's nice – because you never know
How far away it means to go;
And when to-morrow comes, you see,
It may be in the great wide sea.

by Kate Greenaway

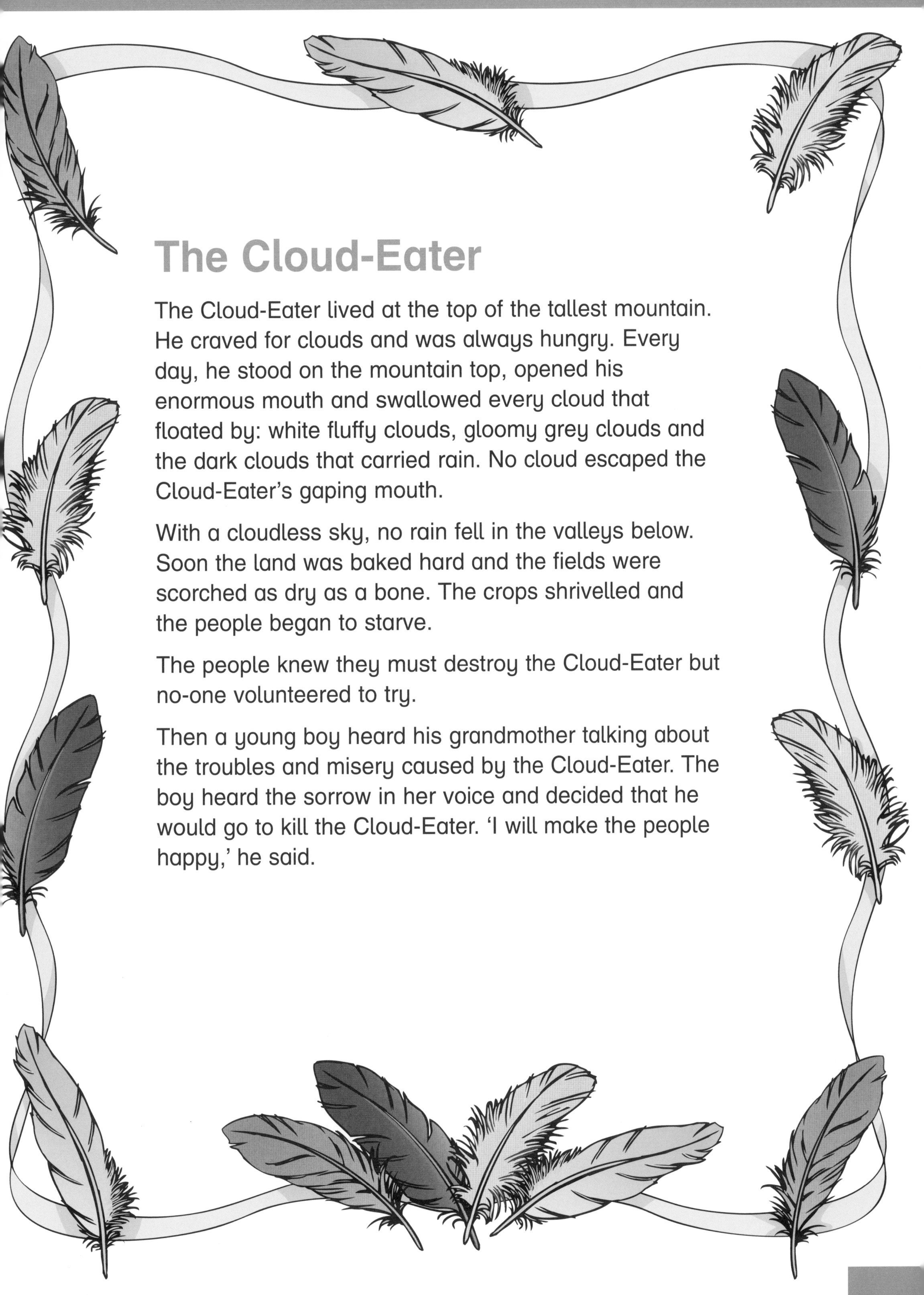

The Cloud-Eater

The Cloud-Eater lived at the top of the tallest mountain. He craved for clouds and was always hungry. Every day, he stood on the mountain top, opened his enormous mouth and swallowed every cloud that floated by: white fluffy clouds, gloomy grey clouds and the dark clouds that carried rain. No cloud escaped the Cloud-Eater's gaping mouth.

With a cloudless sky, no rain fell in the valleys below. Soon the land was baked hard and the fields were scorched as dry as a bone. The crops shrivelled and the people began to starve.

The people knew they must destroy the Cloud-Eater but no-one volunteered to try.

Then a young boy heard his grandmother talking about the troubles and misery caused by the Cloud-Eater. The boy heard the sorrow in her voice and decided that he would go to kill the Cloud-Eater. 'I will make the people happy,' he said.

When his grandmother heard his plan, she felt proud of her grandson and gave him four feathers to take on his journey. 'This red feather will guide you,' she said. 'The blue feather will let you speak the language of animals. The yellow feather will shrink you to the size of the tiniest creature. The black feather will give you strength and courage when you need it most.'

The boy put the red feather in his headband and tucked the others safely in his belt. Off he went, finding the way easily through the maze of trails and hidden mountain paths. As the mountain grew steeper, the boy began to struggle in the sweltering heat. Suddenly, he noticed a strange furry little creature sitting by a hole in the ground. It was a gopher. The boy quickly put the blue feather in his headband and asked the gopher if he knew where to find the Cloud-Eater.

'Yes, my burrow goes so close to the Cloud-Eater that I can sometimes hear him snoring at night,' said the gopher. 'Follow me.'

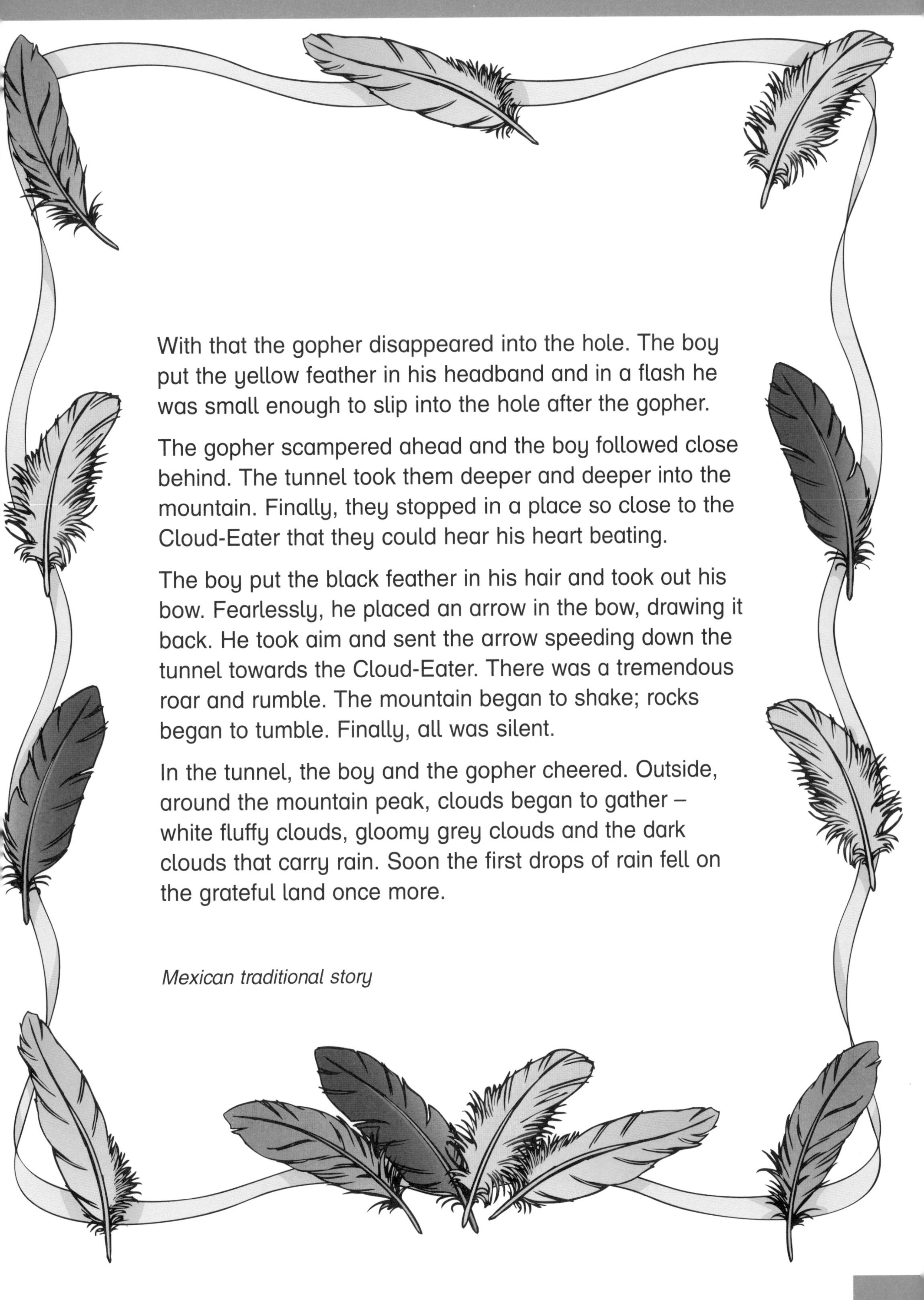

With that the gopher disappeared into the hole. The boy put the yellow feather in his headband and in a flash he was small enough to slip into the hole after the gopher.

The gopher scampered ahead and the boy followed close behind. The tunnel took them deeper and deeper into the mountain. Finally, they stopped in a place so close to the Cloud-Eater that they could hear his heart beating.

The boy put the black feather in his hair and took out his bow. Fearlessly, he placed an arrow in the bow, drawing it back. He took aim and sent the arrow speeding down the tunnel towards the Cloud-Eater. There was a tremendous roar and rumble. The mountain began to shake; rocks began to tumble. Finally, all was silent.

In the tunnel, the boy and the gopher cheered. Outside, around the mountain peak, clouds began to gather – white fluffy clouds, gloomy grey clouds and the dark clouds that carry rain. Soon the first drops of rain fell on the grateful land once more.

Mexican traditional story

Tomatoes

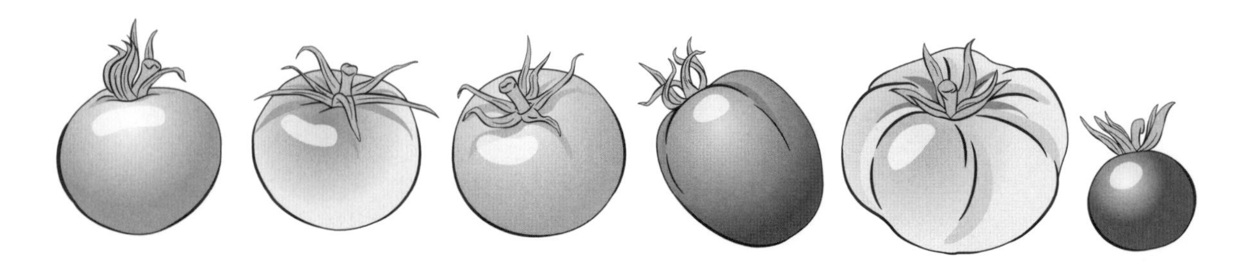

History of the tomato

Tomatoes were first grown for food in southern Mexico thousands of years ago. They were called tomatl, which is where the word 'tomato' comes from.

Tomatoes first arrived in Europe in the sixteenth century, probably brought back by Spanish or Italian explorers.

The very first tomatoes were yellow, so they were named golden apples or pomi d'oro in Italian. The Italian for tomatoes today is pomodoro even though now most tomatoes are red.

To begin with, people in Britain grew tomatoes as decorative plants rather than for food. They thought the bright colour of tomatoes was a danger signal and they were poisonous.

Tomatoes today

Tomatoes today come in all shapes and sizes – from large beefsteak tomatoes to plum tomatoes and baby cherry tomatoes.

Tomatoes are now widely grown all over the world, even as far north as Iceland. In cooler countries, tomatoes are usually grown in greenhouses.

Fact: Tomato seedlings have even been grown in space.

Cooking with tomatoes

Tomatoes are used in cooking all over the world.

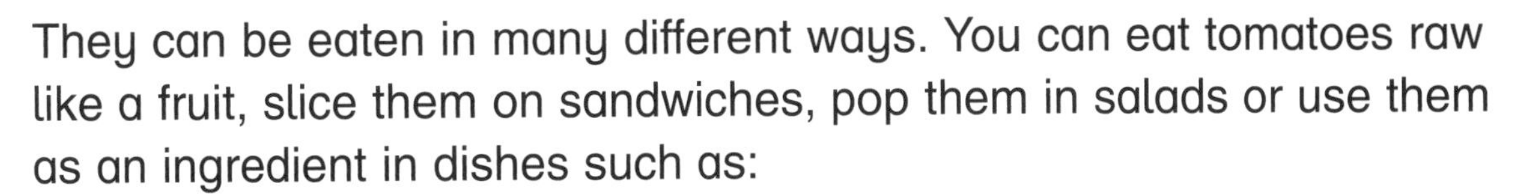

They can be eaten in many different ways. You can eat tomatoes raw like a fruit, slice them on sandwiches, pop them in salads or use them as an ingredient in dishes such as:

- sauces
- salsas
- pizzas
- tomato ketchup
- tomato soup
- tomato juice.

Even unripe green tomatoes are delicious when cooked.

Warning: Don’t eat green tomatoes uncooked – they can cause stomach problems.

You can bake, roast, stew, fry, barbecue or microwave tomatoes.

A super food

Tomatoes are packed with vitamins that help keep you healthy. Scientists believe the bright colours in tomatoes also have important health benefits. Cooked tomatoes are better for you than raw ones.

Tomatoes taste sweet because they contain natural sugars.

Warning: Do not eat the leaves of tomato plants.

Fascinating tomato facts

Fruit or vegetable?

Because the tomato has seeds and grows from a flowering plant, it is really a fruit not a vegetable.

Food festival or food fight?

Each year, in the small Spanish town of Buñol there is a huge food fight where the weapons are 150 000 fat, juicy tomatoes. This messy festival, called La Tomatina, takes place in late August each year. Tens of thousands of people arrive in the town from all over Spain and beyond to take part.

Ketchup on your chips?

Ketchup was not always made from tomatoes. Cookbooks from the nineteenth century have recipes for ketchups made of mushrooms, walnuts, celery, plums and peaches. In fact, the first ketchup was a fish sauce made in southern China.

Red tomatoes?

Most tomatoes are red but you can have yellow, orange, pink and even purple tomatoes!

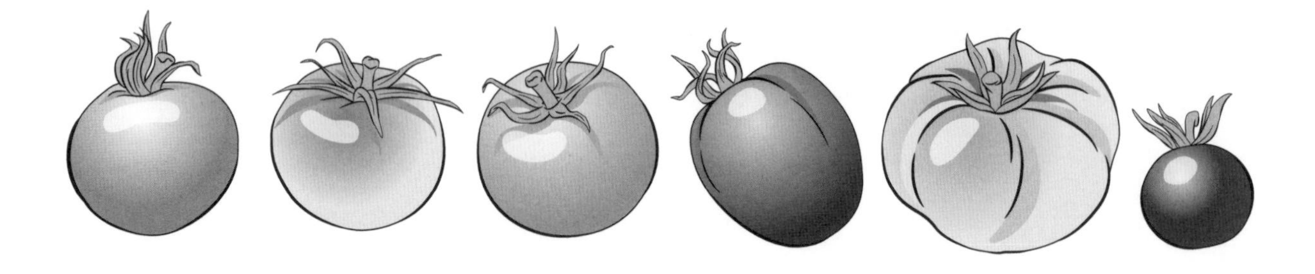

*This is a pull-out section from Schofield & Sims **Key Stage 1 English Practice Papers**. Copyright © Schofield & Sims Ltd, 2016.*

Instructions for the Grammar, Punctuation and Spelling test

The Key Stage 1 Grammar, Punctuation and Spelling test is split into two papers. You should do the papers in this order:

Grammar, Punctuation and Spelling Paper 1: spelling

Grammar, Punctuation and Spelling Paper 2: questions

You are **not** allowed to use a dictionary or a spell checker in these tests.

Instructions for Paper 1: spelling

In this test you will have 20 words to spell. The test will take about 15 minutes but it is not a timed test.

You will need an adult to help you when doing this test.

Note for adults helping with Grammar, Punctuation and Spelling Paper 1: spelling
Before starting the Spelling Test, you will need to remove the instruction pages from this book (found before the answer section). These give you more detailed instructions about the test and tell you the words for the test. They also give you the word for the practice question below.

The adult who is helping you will read out some sentences. You will have the sentences in front of you. Each sentence will have a missing word, like this:

Practice question

I fed the ducks in the ....

The adult will tell you the missing word and you should write it in the gap on the answer page. Make sure you listen carefully to the missing word and spell it correctly.

If you make a mistake, cross it out and write the word again. Make sure your final answer is clear.

After you have finished all 20 questions, you will have a chance to check your spellings and make any changes.

Instructions for Paper 2: questions

This test has questions for you to answer. You have about 20 minutes to answer all the questions but you can have longer if you need it.

Read each question carefully so you know what it is asking.

Types of question

For some questions you need to tick the right box. For some questions you need to write a word, phrase or sentence on a line. Here are some practice questions for you to try.

Practice questions

a Tick the word that completes this sentence.

I am .... to Harry.

Tick **one**.

talk ☐

talked ☐

talking ☐

talks ☐

b Write **one** word on the line below to complete the noun phrase in this sentence.

Saturday was a .... day.

There are other types of question in Paper 2. If you are not sure what to do, read the question carefully and look for the key words that tell you what to do.
For example: Circle..., Draw lines....

Try to answer all of the questions. If you can't answer a question, move on to the next one and come back to it later.

Stop at the end of the test on page 36. The end of the test is clearly marked.

Notes for adults helping with Grammar, Punctuation and Spelling Paper 2: questions
You can help by reading the instructions on this page and checking the child understands what to do before starting the test. Help the child to answer the two practice questions shown above. You should **not** explain any terms used in the questions in the practice paper.

DO NOT TURN OVER THIS PAGE UNTIL YOU ARE READY TO START PAPER 1: SPELLING.

Grammar, Punctuation and Spelling Paper 1: spelling

The adult who is helping you will read out the sentences and tell you what words to write in the gaps. Listen carefully.

1. This pillow is the ....

2. Ben was .... his eyes.

3. He kept the bird in a ....

4. I put the sweet in my ....

5. I have two ....

6. She put all the red .... in the pot.

7. I left the cups in the ....

8. I .... my feet to keep them warm.

9. I was late for .... on Monday.

10. We need .... to eat our ice cream.

please turn over

11. I saw a .... gold ring on the grass.

12. The children .... on the paper.

13. The rain made a big .... on the floor.

14. My cat has very long ....

15. The vase was .... a lot of money.

16. Dad .... the box down the stairs.

17. Did you .... my name?

18. I like .... about pirates.

19. There were lots of shells on the ....

20. Mum was .... when she saw the present.

END OF TEST

Total score for Paper 1: spelling
Write this score in the box on pages 3 and 51.

Grammar, Punctuation and Spelling Paper 2: questions

1 Draw lines to match the sentences below with the punctuation mark needed to complete them. One has been done for you.

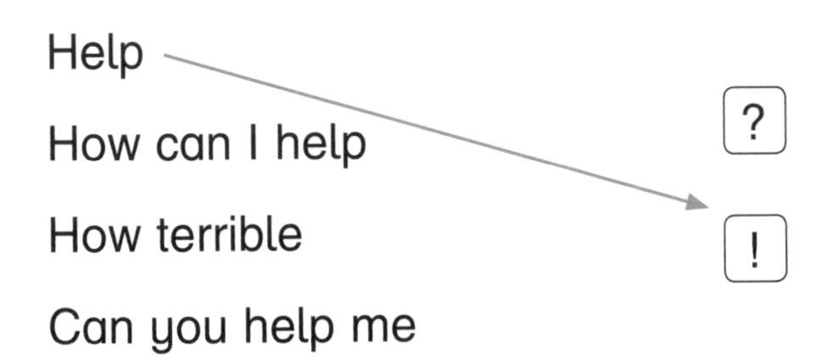

2 Tick the correct word to complete the sentence below.

Ellie wanted to go swimming .... she forgot her towel.

Tick **one**.

and ☐

but ☐

or ☐

so ☐

3 Circle the words in the sentence below that must have a **capital letter**.

next tuesday megan is going on holiday to spain.

page 31 total

please turn over

4 What type of word is underlined in the sentence below?

The boy put on his baggy jumper.

Tick **one**.

a noun ☐

a verb ☐

an adjective ☐

an adverb ☐

5 Write **s** or **es** to make each word a plural.

bus ....

sweet ....

dish ....

6 Look at where the arrow is pointing.

We waited in the park all morning ↑ Jake was late.

Which punctuation mark is missing?

Tick **one**.

comma ☐

question mark ☐

full stop ☐

exclamation mark ☐

7 Tick to show whether each sentence is a **statement** or a **command**.

Sentence	**Statement**	**Command**
Ruby is in the sandpit.		
Come and sit on the bench.		
Don't scare the ducks.		
I like playing on the swings.		

8 Tick one box to show where a **comma** should go in the sentence below.

Tick **one**.

I played football with Ben Erin and Sam this morning.

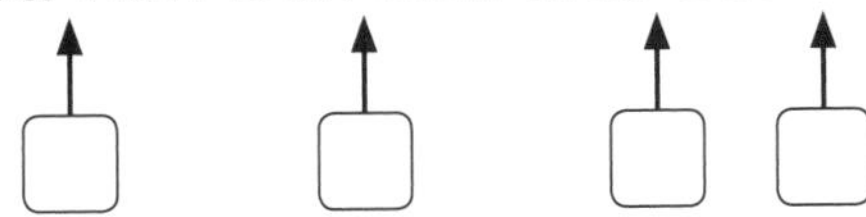

9 What type of word is <u>fence</u> in the sentence below?

A bird sat on the wooden fence singing happily.

Tick **one**.

an adjective ☐

an adverb ☐

a noun ☐

a verb ☐

pages 32–33 total

please turn over

10 Circle the **three verbs** in the sentence below.

It was breakfast time and Tom ate his toast as Dad hung the washing on the line.

11 Tick the sentence that is correct.

Tick **one**.

The dog ran to the gate and bark. ☐

The dog ran to the gate and barks. ☐

The dog ran to the gate and barked. ☐

The dog run to the gate and barked. ☐

12 Tick **one** box to show which word is an **adverb**.

The old lady spoke kindly to the little girl.

☐ ☐ ☐ ☐

13 Tick the word to best complete the sentence below.

I chose this scarf .... I liked the colour.

Tick **one**.

if ☐

that ☐

because ☐

when ☐

14 Write the words did not as **one** word, using an apostrophe.

I .... see you hiding in the corner.

15 Write **one** word on the line below to complete the sentence in the **present tense**.

The children .... helping Mrs Jackson.

16 Circle the suffix needed to complete the word **dark** in the sentence below.

A tiger hid in the **dark** .... of the forest.

er   ly   ness   ment

17 The verbs in the boxes are in the present tense. Write these verbs in the **past tense**.

sees   chases

Lily .... her friend and .... after him.

pages 34–35 total

please turn over

18 Tick the sentence that has the correct punctuation.

Tick **one**.

I've found Katies shoes. ☐

Ive found Katie's shoes. ☐

I've found Katie's shoes. ☐

Iv'e found Katie's shoes. ☐

19 Mum comes home and finds lots of people waiting to give her a surprise party.

a) Write an exclamation that Mum might say. Remember to use correct punctuation.

What ....

b) Write a question that Mum might ask. Remember to use correct punctuation.

What ....

END OF TEST

page total

Total score for Paper 2: Questions
Write this score in the box on pages 3 and 51.

Script for Grammar, Punctuation and Spelling Paper 1

(for adult helper)

The spelling test should take about 15 minutes but it is not a timed test.

Before you start

Before you start the spelling test, remove this page from the book. This page gives you the script and instructions for carrying out the test.

Use the instruction page (page 27) to introduce the test, explaining that you are going to read out some sentences, each of which has a missing word. You will say the missing word so the child can write it in the space.

Do the practice question on the instruction page to check the child understands what to do. The practice word is: **park**.

Carrying out the test

Once the child understands what to do, you can begin the test. Tell the child to turn to pages 29 and 30.

You will need to read the questions out from the reverse of this page.

Read the 20 spellings like this:

1. Give the spelling number: *Spelling 1*
2. Say: *The word is... [softest]*
3. Read the full sentence: *This pillow is the softest.*
4. Repeat: *The word is... [softest]*

Leave at least 12 seconds between spellings. You can repeat the target word if necessary.

After question 20, read all 20 sentences again so the child can check their spellings and make any changes.

continued overleaf

1. This pillow is the softest.

2. Ben was rubbing his eyes.

3. He kept the bird in a cage.

4. I put the sweet in my mouth.

5. I have two sisters.

6. She put all the red crayons in the pot.

7. I left the cups in the kitchen.

8. I stamped my feet to keep them warm.

9. I was late for school on Monday.

10. We need spoons to eat our ice cream.

11. I saw a shiny gold ring on the grass.

12. The children wrote on the paper.

13. The rain made a big puddle on the floor.

14. My cat has very long whiskers.

15. The vase was worth a lot of money.

16. Dad carried the box down the stairs.

17. Did you mention my name?

18. I like stories about pirates.

19. There were lots of shells on the seashore.

20. Mum was speechless when she saw the present.

From Schofield & Sims ***Key Stage 1 English Practice Papers****. Copyright © Schofield & Sims Ltd, 2016.*

Answers and mark scheme

Reading Paper 1

Record the mark awarded for each question. Half marks cannot be awarded. The 'What is being tested?' column provides cross-references to relevant information in the **Key Stage 1 English Revision Guide**.

Question	Required answer	Marks	What is being tested?
1	Award **1 mark** for an answer that refers to food or something to eat.	1 mark	Identify relevant details from fiction texts (for example, about events) Understanding the story page 10
2	Award **1 mark** for **both** correct options ticked. inside the washerman's house ✓ under the window ✓	1 mark	Identify relevant details from fiction texts (for example, about events) Understanding the story page 10
3	Award **1 mark** for answers that refer to what the jackal says, for example: • because he says he didn't look like a jackal any more • because he thinks the others will laugh at him Also accept answers that refer to the jackal sighing or walking slowly.	1 mark	Make simple inference from the text (for example, about a character's feelings) Thinking about characters page 13
4	Award **1 mark** for: terror	1 mark	Draw on knowledge of vocabulary to understand texts Understanding word meanings page 6
5	Award **1 mark** for the correct option ticked. pleased ✓	1 mark	Make simple inference from the text (for example, about a character's feelings) Thinking about characters page 13
6	Award **1 mark** for: they bowed down Accept also: they said, 'You are our king!'	1 mark	Identify relevant details from fiction texts (for example, about events) Understanding the story page 10

Question	Required answer	Marks	What is being tested?
7	Award **1 mark** for an explanation that refers to the effect of the blue colour on the other animals, for example: • they think the colour makes him special • they think it is the colour of kings • the colour gives him power over the other animals	1 mark	Make simple inference from the text Explaining why page 11
8	Award **1 mark** for correct matching. lions — fed him mice — made his bed elephants — gave him water monkeys — kept him cool	1 mark	Identify relevant details from fiction texts (for example, about characters and events) Following a story page 8
9	Award **1 mark** for an explanation referring to the other jackals knowing the truth, for example: • they knew/would know he was just a jackal • they would tell the other animals his secret/he was just a jackal	1 mark	Make simple inference from the text Explaining why page 11
10	Award **1 mark** for the correct option ticked. he was treated too well ✓	1 mark	Identify relevant details from fiction texts (for example, about events) Understanding the story page 10
11	Award **1 mark** for the correct option ticked. not special ✓	1 mark	Draw on knowledge of vocabulary to understand texts Understanding word meanings page 6
12	Award **1 mark** for the correct option ticked. he pretended to be something he was not ✓	1 mark	Make general inferences Thinking about the story page 12
13	Award **1 mark** for the correct order. the jackal returned to the forest 2 the jackal's fur was dyed blue 1 the jackal was tricked by the other jackals 4 the jackal tricked the other animals 3	1 mark	Identify the sequence of events in texts Following a story page 8
14	Award **1 mark** for the correct option ticked. to help them slide ✓	1 mark	Retrieve relevant details from non-fiction to demonstrate understanding of information Finding information page 18

Question	Required answer	Marks	What is being tested?
15	Award **1 mark** for **both** of the following: • a layer of fat/fat tummy or belly • waterproof feathers	1 mark	Retrieve relevant details from non-fiction to demonstrate understanding of information Information from pictures page 19
16	Award **1 mark** for the correct option ticked. spiky ✓	1 mark	Draw on knowledge of vocabulary to understand texts Understanding word meanings page 6
17	Award **1 mark** for an answer that refers to catching food, for example: • to catch their food • because they catch all their food underwater • because they need to catch fish to eat	1 mark	Retrieve relevant details to explain ideas or information in non-fiction texts Explaining information page 21
18	Award **1 mark** for the correct option ticked. Emperor penguins lay eggs in spring. ✓	1 mark	Retrieve relevant details from non-fiction to demonstrate understanding of information Finding information page 18
19	Award **1 mark** for an answer that refers to keeping it warm, for example: • to keep it warm • because it would be too cold on the ice	1 mark	Make simple inference from the text Explaining information page 21
20	Award **1 mark** for: cosy Accept also: tucked Do not accept 'tucked up' as this is two words.	1 mark	Draw on knowledge of vocabulary to understand texts Understanding word meanings page 6

Reading Paper 2

Record the mark awarded for each question. No half marks can be awarded. Where a question is worth 2 marks follow the advice on whether to award 0, 1 or 2 marks. The 'What is being tested?' column provides cross-references to relevant information in the **Key Stage 1 English Revision Guide**.

Question	Required answer	Marks	What is being tested?
1	Award **1 mark** for the correct option ticked. over a river ✓	1 mark	Make simple inferences based on the text Reading poems page 14
2	Award **1 mark** for **all three** of the following: • a [little] fish • a water rat • a spider	1 mark	Retrieve relevant details to demonstrate understanding Reading poems page 14
3	Award **1 mark** for the correct option ticked. big ✓	1 mark	Draw on knowledge of vocabulary to understand texts Understanding word meanings page 6
4	Award **1 mark** for **each** of the following ideas (the ideas do not have to be in this order) Idea 1: throw stones in the water and watch the circles they make (1 mark) Idea 2: to make a boat out of a flower and watch it float away down the river (1 mark)	max. 2 marks	Retrieve and explain relevant details from the poem Reading poems page 14
5	Award **1 mark** for answers referring to being close to clouds, for example: • because he liked eating clouds • because that's where there are lots of clouds • so he could catch clouds in his mouth	1 mark	Make simple inference from the text Explaining why page 11
6	Award **1 mark** for **both** of the following: baked [hard] scorched **Do not** accept 'shrivelled' as this describes the crops, not the ground.	1 mark	Draw on knowledge of vocabulary to understand texts Understanding word meanings page 6

Question	Required answer	Marks	What is being tested?
7	Award **1 mark** for a reason/motive derived from the text, for example: • because he wanted to make the people happy • because his grandmother was sad • because he wanted to help the village/the people	1 mark	Identify and explain key aspects of fiction texts, such as character motives, events Thinking about characters page 13
8	Award **1 mark** for reasons that can be inferred from the text, for example: • because he is going to do something dangerous • because he is very brave to try to kill the Cloud-Eater • because he is volunteering when no-one else would • because he is doing something to help the people	1 mark	Make inference from the text Explaining why and Thinking about characters pages 11 and 13
9	Award **1 mark** for an answer that refers to the red feather, for example: • because he had the red feather • because his grandmother had given him the red feather	1 mark	Make simple inference from the text Explaining why page 11
10	Award **1 mark** for an answer that refers to the silence, for example: • because it went silent • because they couldn't hear his heart beating • because all the noise stopped	1 mark	Make simple inference from the text Explaining why page 11
11	Award **1 mark** for the correct matching. the red feather – helped him find the gopher the blue feather – helped him ask the way the yellow feather – helped him get close to the Cloud-Eater the black feather – helped him fire the arrow	1 mark	Identify key details about events in stories Following a story page 8

Question	Required answer	Marks	What is being tested?
12	Award **2 marks** for a plausible prediction **and** a reason that is based on something in the text, for example: • I think everyone will be very happy and there will be a big celebration because it has started to rain and their crops will grow again • I think his grandmother will be very proud of him because he has killed the Cloud-Eater • I think the people will give him a reward because he has saved them Award **1 mark** for a plausible prediction without a text-based reason.	max. 2 marks	Make simple and general predictions based on the text Following a story and Thinking about the story pages 8 and 12
13	Award **1 mark** for a reference to them being thought poisonous, for example: because people thought they were poisonous	1 mark	Retrieve relevant details from non-fiction to explain understanding of information Finding information page 18
14	Award **1 mark** for a reference to them needing warmth, for example: • because it's too cold to grow them outside • because they need sun/warmth • because it is too cold in some countries/places	1 mark	Make simple inference from the text Explaining information page 21
15	Award **1 mark** for **three** of the following: • in a salad • tomato juice • [sliced] in a sandwich • salsa • like a fruit	1 mark	Identify key information from a non-fiction text Finding information page 18
16	Award **1 mark** for the correct option ticked. fish ☑	1 mark	Identify key information from a non-fiction text Finding information page 18
17	Award **1 mark** for reference to the number of people who attend, for example: because people come from all over Spain/the world to take part	1 mark	Make simple inference from the text Explaining information page 21

<table>
<tr><th>Question</th><th>Required answer</th><th>Marks</th><th>What is being tested?</th></tr>
<tr><td>18</td><td>Award 1 mark for all boxes correctly ticked.
<table>
<tr><th>The information says that...</th><th>True</th><th>False</th></tr>
<tr><td>Tomatoes are vegetables.</td><td></td><td>✓</td></tr>
<tr><td>Tomatoes are the fruit of the tomato plant.</td><td>✓</td><td></td></tr>
<tr><td>The bright colours in tomatoes are good for you.</td><td>✓</td><td></td></tr>
<tr><td>Today all tomatoes are red.</td><td></td><td>✓</td></tr>
<tr><td>Tomato plants are not good to eat.</td><td>✓</td><td></td></tr>
</table></td><td>1 mark</td><td>Identify key information from a non-fiction text
Finding information
page 18</td></tr>
</table>

Grammar, Punctuation and Spelling Paper 1: spelling

After the spelling test, check the child's spelling of each word using the table below. The 'What is being tested?' column provides cross-references to relevant information in the **Key Stage 1 English Revision Guide**.

Question	Word	Marks	What is being tested?
1	softest	1 mark	Adding –er and –est to adjectives where no change is needed to the root word Adding –ing and –ed (–er, –est, –y) page 39
2	rubbing	1 mark	Adding –ing, –ed, –er, –est, –y to short words ending in a single consonant letter Adding –ing and –ed (–er, –est, –y) page 39
3	cage	1 mark	The / j / sound is spelt 'ge' at the end of words Special spellings page 40
4	mouth	1 mark	Spelling vowel digraphs Spelling long vowel sounds page 34
5	sisters	1 mark	Adding –s and –es to words Adding –s and –es page 38
6	crayons	1 mark	Spelling vowel digraphs Spelling long vowel sounds page 34
7	kitchen	1 mark	Using k for the / k / sound; the / ch / sound spelt 'tch' Special spellings page 40
8	stamped	1 mark	Adding the endings –ing, –ed and –er to verbs where no change is needed to the root word Adding –ing and –ed (–er, –est, –y) page 39
9	school	1 mark	Common exception words Learning to spell tricky words page 42
10	spoons	1 mark	Spelling vowel digraphs Spelling long vowel sounds page 34
11	shiny	1 mark	Adding the endings –ing, –ed, –er, –est and –y to words ending in –e Adding –ing and –ed (–er, –est, –y) page 39

Question	Word	Marks	What is being tested?
12	wrote	1 mark	The / r / sound spelt 'wr' at the beginning of words Special spellings page 40
13	puddle	1 mark	–le at the end of words Word endings page 37
14	whiskers	1 mark	New consonant spellings 'ph' and 'wh' Special spellings page 40
15	worth	1 mark	The 'or' spelling after w Using spelling patterns page 41
16	carried	1 mark	Adding –ed, –ing, –er, and –est to a word ending in consonant –y Adding –ing and –ed (–er, –est, –y) page 39
17	mention	1 mark	Words ending –tion Word endings page 37
18	stories	1 mark	Adding –es to nouns and verbs ending in –y Adding –s and –es page 38
19	seashore	1 mark	Compound words Spelling longer words page 36
20	speechless	1 mark	The suffixes –ment, –ness, –ful, –less and –ly Spelling longer words page 36

Grammar, Punctuation and Spelling Paper 2: questions

Record the mark awarded for each question. No half marks can be awarded. The 'What is being tested?' column provides cross references to relevant information in the **Key Stage 1 English Revision Guide**.

Question	Required answer	Marks	What is being tested?
1	Award **1 mark** for **all three** matched correctly. How can I help — ? How terrible — ! Can you help me — ?	1 mark	Question marks and exclamation marks to demarcate sentences Question marks and exclamation marks page 29
2	Award **1 mark** for the correct box ticked. but ✓	1 mark	Co-ordinating conjunctions – **or, and** and **but** Joining ideas together – and, but, or page 23
3	Award **1 mark** for **all four** identified. (next)(tuesday)(megan) is going on holiday to (spain).	1 mark	Capital letters for names of people, places and days of the week More capital letters page 30
4	Award **1 mark** for the correct box ticked. an adjective ✓	1 mark	Grammatical terms/word classes – adjectives Using describing words page 26
5	Award **1 mark** for **all three** correct suffixes added. buses sweets dishes	1 mark	Regular plural noun suffixes –s or –es Adding –s and –es page 38
6	Award **1 mark** for the correct box ticked. full stop ✓	1 mark	Full stops to demarcate sentences Capital letters and full stops page 28
7	Award **1 mark** for **all four** correct. (see table below)	1 mark	Grammatical patterns in a sentence – statements and commands Writing in sentences page 22

Sentence	S	C
Ruby is in the sandpit.	✓	
Come and sit on the bench.		✓
Don't scare the ducks.		✓
I like playing on the swings.	✓	

Question	Required answer	Marks	What is being tested?
8	Award **1 mark** for the correct box ticked. I played football with Ben ✓ Erin and Sam this morning.	1 mark	Commas to separate items in a list Commas and inverted commas page 31
9	Award **1 mark** for the correct box ticked. a noun ✓	1 mark	Grammatical terms/word classes – nouns Using describing words page 26
10	Award **1 mark** for **all three** identified. It (was) breakfast time and Tom (ate) his toast as Dad (hung) the washing on the line.	1 mark	Grammatical terms/word classes – verbs Using describing words and Past and present tense pages 26–27
11	Award **1 mark** for the correct box ticked. The dog ran to the gate and barked. ✓	1 mark	Tense consistency Past and present tense page 27
12	Award **1 mark** for the correct box ticked. kindly ✓	1 mark	Grammatical terms/word classes – adverbs Using describing words page 26
13	Award **1 mark** for the correct box ticked. because ✓	1 mark	Subordinating conjunctions – using **when, if, that, because** More joining words page 24
14	Award **1 mark** for: didn't	1 mark	Apostrophes to mark contracted forms Apostrophes page 32
15	Award **1 mark** for: are	1 mark	Use of the progressive form of verbs in the present and past tense Past and present tense page 27
16	Award **1 mark** for the correct suffix circled. (ness)	1 mark	Formation of nouns using suffixes –ness, –ment, –er Prefixes and suffixes page 7
17	Award **1 mark** for: **saw** and **chased**	1 mark	Simple past and present tense Past and present tense page 27

Question	Required answer	Marks	What is being tested?
18	Award **1 mark** for the correct box ticked. I've found Katie's shoes. ✓	1 mark	Apostrophes to mark singular possession in nouns and apostrophes to mark contracted forms Apostrophes page 32
19	a Award **1 mark** for an appropriate exclamation that ends with an exclamation mark, for example: What a surprise!	1 mark	Grammatical patterns in an exclamation Question marks and exclamation marks page 29
	b Award **1 mark** for an appropriate question that ends with a question mark, for example: What are you all doing here? What is going on?	1 mark	Grammatical patterns in a question Question marks and exclamation marks page 29

Total marks

Ask the adult to write the total marks of each test in the boxes below.

Reading Paper 1 (marks out of 20)

Reading Paper 2 (marks out of 20)

Total marks for the Reading test (out of 40)

Grammar, Punctuation and Spelling Paper 1
(marks out of 20)

Grammar, Punctuation and Spelling Paper 2
(marks out of 20)

Total marks for the Grammar, Punctuation and Spelling test (out of 40)

What your score means

Check your mark for each test (out of 40) against the scores below.

Above 31 You are already achieving a good score and understand many of the things expected of you. There are still a few things you need to work on. Have a look at the questions you answered incorrectly. See if you can work out where you went wrong.

24–31 You already know and understand many of the things expected of you but there are still some key areas you need to work on. Ask an adult to look at the 'What is being tested?' column with you for the words and questions you answered incorrectly. This will show you the things you need to revise.

Below 24 You know and understand some of the things expected of you but there are still a number of areas you need to work on to help you answer questions like those in the test. Ask an adult to help you revise the topics that you found difficult.

Revision Guide

The Schofield & Sims **Key Stage 1 English Revision Guide** can help you with revising the things you need to work on. It covers all the grammar, punctuation and spelling topics and includes information on fiction, non-fiction and poetry. There are also Test Yourself questions and a helpful glossary where you can look up any words that you didn't understand in the practice papers.

Schofield&Sims

the long-established educational publisher specialising in maths, English and science

The **Key Stage 1 English Practice Papers** contained in this book reflect the appearance and content of the national tests at Key Stage 1. Papers on reading, grammar, punctuation and spelling are included, as well as full instructions and detailed mark schemes. Cross-references to the separate **Key Stage 1 English Revision Guide** allow children and adult helpers to tailor revision for exam success.

The Schofield & Sims **Practice Papers** are closely matched to the National Curriculum test frameworks and help children to revise what they have learnt at school, in preparation for the end of key stage tests. Detailed instructions on using the papers, and guidance on equipment and timings, provide reassurance and help children to become familiar with a more formal test situation.

Five Schofield & Sims **Practice Papers** books are available, providing rigorous practice in maths and English at Key Stages 1 and 2, as well as science at Key Stage 2.

The **Practice Papers** feature:

- formal exam-style questions, similar to those found in the national tests
- comprehensive instructions for both the child and adult helper
- a clear mark scheme with additional comments and guidance
- cross-references to relevant information in the corresponding revision guide.

Key Stage 1 Maths
Revision Guide
ISBN 978 07217 1360 1

Key Stage 1 English
Revision Guide
ISBN 978 07217 1364 9

Key Stage 1 Science
Revision Guide
ISBN 978 07217 1368 7

Key Stage 1 Maths
Practice Papers
ISBN 978 07217 1362 5

Key Stage 1 English
Practice Papers
ISBN 978 07217 1366 3

For further information and to place your order visit www.schofieldandsims.co.uk or telephone 01484 607080

ISBN 978 07217 1366 3
Key Stage 1
Age range 5–7 years
£3.95 (Retail price)